The Receptionist
and Other Tales

Conversation Pieces

A Small Paperback Series from Aqueduct Press
Subscriptions available: www.aqueductpress.com

About the Aqueduct Press Conversation Pieces Series

The feminist engaged with sf is passionately interested in challenging the way things are, passionately determined to understand how everything works. It is my constant sense of our feminist-sf present as a grand conversation that enables me to trace its existence into the past and from there see its trajectory extending into our future. A genealogy for feminist sf would not constitute a chart depicting direct lineages but would offer us an ever-shifting, fluid mosaic, the individual tiles of which we will probably only ever partially access. What could be more in the spirit of feminist sf than to conceptualize a genealogy that explicitly manifests our own communities across not only space but also time?

Aqueduct's small paperback series, Conversation Pieces, aims to both document and facilitate the "grand conversation." The Conversation Pieces series presents a wide variety of texts, including short fiction (which may not always be sf and may not necessarily even be feminist), essays, speeches, manifestoes, poetry, interviews, correspondence, and group discussions. Many of the texts are reprinted material, but some are new. The grand conversation reaches at least as far back as Mary Shelley and extends, in our speculations and visions, into the continually-created future. In Jonathan Goldberg's words, "To look forward to the history that will be, one must look at and retell the history that has been told." And that is what Conversation Pieces is all about.

L. Timmel Duchamp

Jonathan Goldberg, "The History That Will Be" in Louise Fradenburg and Carla Freccero, eds., *Premodern Sexualities* (New York and London: Routledge, 1996)

Conversation Pieces
Volume 33

The Receptionist
and Other Tales

poems by

Lesley Wheeler

Published by Aqueduct Press
PO Box 95787
Seattle, WA 98145-2787
www.aqueductpress.com

ISBN: 978-1-61976-012-7

Cover painting: *Studies of Angela* (detail),
courtesy of Rosemary Starace.
www.rosemarystarace.com

Book Design by Kathryn Wilham
Original Block Print of Mary Shelley by Justin Kempton:
www.writersmugs.com

for Cameron Wheeler Gavaler

Contents

I
The Receptionist

1. THE FIRST TRANSMISSION

"He knocked three times on the castle door,"
Edna read, closing the gold and purple cover,
soothing their howls, leaving one with a score

of plastic knights, the other hunched over
a drawing-pad, sketching ghosts. Her husband
was on evening shifts again—happy shiver,

airy quiet before her, hours on end,
stacked like blocks or sandwiches. Just pack
lunches first, scrub down the counters, attend

to cooling laundry, set the alarm, lock
what's ajar, then glorious pajama-clad nothing.
It was after she drew curtains against the black

windows, after the kettle had begun to sing,
while she served cat-food to a yowling beast
on a pretty saucer, that the telephone rang

three times. Edna held her breath—please,
no talking. The shrilling stopped. Then she heard a voice.
It wasn't a remembered sound, or the chill breeze

of conscience saying *one more chore*, or boys
fussing upstairs. *Okay*, it told her from her right
shoulder, or maybe the side of her skull. *Good choice:*

mutinous. Let's say your stepmother's light
blew out just then, and she tsked and cut the line.
By the time she changes the bulb her favorite

show will be on, so she'll leave you alone
to consider your duties. It wasn't a whisper she knew.
It wasn't a child or a woman or a man.

She turned off the burner, poured water through
a leafy teabag, and paused, listening for more.
The first revolution: simply to refuse.

2. DAWN RITES

The trees, next morning, flared like yellow torches
against the frowning battlements of the College
where Edna worked. She stepped over two flat roaches,

brown as tea leaves—these old buildings itched
with them—and unlocked the narrow door. Her office
was also the department's closet, kitchen,

and inner chamber, where professors hissed
hexes and plotted coups as if Edna could
not hear them. At this hour, with lids of mist

still clapped over low roads, most of them would
hunker over notebooks, practicing spells.
She powered up the computer, hooked her hood

behind the door, mounded up fragrant hills
of coffee in the filter, sat down at her desk
to simmer and wait at the lip of her screen's well.

White characters shimmered there, were whisked
away by shifting light. It winked and then,
like a pool in some enchanted place, it asked

her for a password before it granted visions.
She shook her head to clear it—too many fantasy
read-alouds lately, all dark lords and minions.

Her messages rose up, ordinary
questions: would you please, what's the plan.
Bold and steaming. She scanned them, feeling slightly

disappointed. It was well after ten,
after the clatter of mugs and boots, copies hot
for class, when Edna thought to check her spam.

There it was, from "Gnomic Utterance." Subject
line: *Solve for X*. My destiny approaches,
she thought, and chuckled like a cracked crock-pot.

3. INTERPRETING RUNES

The message: *You will find companions at the inn.*
No signature. Then, with her green heels drumming
applause, the drama professor billowed in,

followed close by the work-song-humming
medievalist. Edna dimmed her crystal
ball discreetly with a click. Her pulse was thrumming.

"The Dean," Galina declared, "is a scoundrel."
Her role: Head of Women's Studies. Her métier:
to hex his sly designs. Galina filled

the temporary gig with vigor, too straight
for his crooked script. "Edna, good morning,"
Galina said, and spun her tale of foul play.

The medievalist made sympathetic crooning
sounds in his beard. Edna wondered why
he was clutching a hammer. Some drooping

diploma? The Victorianist sidled
in, shied out, during the scene. Elfin and fair,
he would have been almost unbearably fine

if his mouth had not been shadowed by a sneer.
Edna listened covertly to the list
of grievances and pretended to stare

at the course-scheduling spreadsheet. She missed
working with Monique, the oracle
of campus combat—medic, too. Her best

friend, though, was managing claims at the hospital.
Then she understood. Jackson's Tavern. Edna's
father wouldn't mind keeping his beautiful

grandkids for one more hour. She could buzz
Monique who, yes, would love a glass of wine
at five, no special occasion, just because.

4. In Which a Consultation Is Cut Short by a Brawl

"Is the Dragon involved?" Monique inquired, sleek head
bent over a mojito, tone low. "No."
The Dragon broods over a glittering hoard

of Renaissance lyrics, but a few years ago
she had glanced up once, noticed the president
gutting the curriculum, and was so

enraged she crisped him with a single vent
from her aged jowls. "Then these complaints
   don't matter,"
Monique judged. "Galina's a malcontent,

they think. If she says it, they won't hear."
Edna grunted. The bar was crowded tonight,
some finance guys back-slapping at the bar,

the paranoid untenured hiding from the light
with their chocolate martinis and local ales.
Edna longed to tell all but couldn't quite

decide on how to pour: fast, without details,
like water for thirst? At a tilt, so the foam
doesn't mount too high in the glass, the tale

too frothy to swallow? As Edna played for time,
pinching the stem of a chardonnay, she saw
a disturbance in the corner of the room.

A tall woman, haughty—Edna didn't know
her, though she joked with a group of professors,
including the department's new poet. A guffaw,

some iced smirks, and suddenly a cup turned over.
The mocker toppled it, aiming surely,
and then swept away, baubles agleam. The poor

bard was whisking liquor as demurely
as she could from her skimpy dress. A threat
or an insult, not a joke. Aggression, purely.

5.   A REEK OF WRONGNESS

Edna snagged the bard's eye, shared a miserable
smile before the damp poet hurried
out. She told Monique, "Her name is Isabel,

and she's pining in exile." Edna couldn't read
the verse—ragged jumbles that were meant
to subvert patriarchal discourse, impede

the grammar of law, fracture and circumvent
hegemony—but felt sorry for this underfed
person ever revising a constantly-

rejected manuscript (Edna managed
her submissions). "Well, just keep her clear
of that Dean," Monique replied as she counted

out bills, her poise unstitched. It was a year
since Monique had fled the College, touched too many
times by the wolf in wool, while no one would hear

her protest at his bullying. "Nothing so tasty
as a postmodern Latina with a weak tenure file."
Monique, now scarved, exhaled scratchily

as Edna hugged her goodbye, stepped into the mild
evening, began to walk to her parents' house.
Monique had been dating a professor while

his hounding unraveled her life, a woman named Bess
in Chemistry and in the closet. Dr. Evil
had wooed Bess for Associate Dean, with success,

and she had broken with Monique. The upheaval
shredded staff morale, but he survived,
all who crossed him swept out with the rubble.

Even Bess looked frayed now, hunched
into herself…Edna faltered. Trouble.
On the hill ahead, in leather, silver-knived.

6. HILL-TOP AMBUSH

University Counsel loomed there, a pair
of lawyers, Blackberrys shining brighter than
the hide on their wings. *This is the part where*

the Riders attack you from their avian
steeds. The damned Voice tolled again in Edna's
ear, and she looked up in surprise. A skin

of clouds was forming over faint stars,
a crescent moon. *They want to steal your voice,*
it warned. Not my amulet? Edna was

exasperated. Not my spell-book? *Your choice.*
She didn't know what that meant, but she did
wear her mother's school ring. Feeling daft, she toyed

with it, twisted the garnet around, hid
the stone in her fist. Of course, she was already
invisible. The Dean's defenders slid

downhill, vile beaks clicking. Edna held steady.
Lucky for you—was that a mocking tone?—
the Broken Harp is here. Lights dawned ahead,

a car pulled up, the passenger window down.
"Want a ride?" Isabel asked with an absurd
grin. Edna smiled back and climbed on in.

A rush of wind, a frustrated cry, and the birds
swept past. Isabel's face was streaked, her grief
unblotted, but in a normal voice she observed,

"Dark early these days. Where do you live?"
"Oh, I'll pick up my kids at my father's house,
just down the next street, and walk from there." Disbelief.

"The block with all the mansions?" She thinks I'm a mouse,
Edna thought, and suddenly, she couldn't bear
it. Not smallness. Not silence. Her pride aroused.

7. LOST BIRTHRIGHT

"My family has been here for generations,"
Edna said. "My great-grandfather served
as President at the College's foundation."

Edna fingered the ring again, unnerved
to be looked at, finally. "Then how did you—
why on earth are you—" Isabel swerved

around a roadblock of trash bins, turned onto Yew
Street, rolled to a stop. "I don't understand."
Dry air sighed from the vents. Everyone just knew

Edna's tale in this small town; she had no canned
version to open and project. "My mother,
she taught here, two poets before you," she began,

awkwardly. "She was sick with cancer
most of my girlhood, it was kind of… Well,
she finally died when I was a senior

applying to college. She wanted me in school,
so I packed up and left, but you know how some students
hold on much better than you think they will

through a crisis, then they just collapse?"
Isabel sat attentive, still, now.
"So you came back and stayed," she whispered. Perhaps

Isabel was thinking of her own
mother, in Queens. Her face had gone soft, those black
eyebrows wrung like a handkerchief. Her eyes won

Edna over. "Yes. But really, I like
making coffee." Suddenly both were snorting
with laughter, choking on it, hysterical,

weeping a little, Isabel's keys still ticking
against the steering column. Edna had found
her at the inn. Was the plot finally clicking?

8.   Interlude with Random Villagers

Saturday was always soccer games,
canvas chairs unfolded on the grass,
cicadas waiting for the sun to warm

their flimsy legs. Edna liked to bask
too with a book, while her spouse patrolled the verge
of the field vigilantly, quick to harass

the ump. Her husband loved to coach, to urge
on the timid kids who flee the ball,
waken the dreamers, tame the ones who surge

recklessly after every goal and stall
mid-game, blood sugar exhausted. She wanted
mainly a bit of yellow light, the fall

brilliance shining on her boy's damp head.
The younger one pounded towards her, sweaty, sent
aside for a rest; she handed him a red

water-bottle, listened to his lament
about cheaters on the other team, stroked
his skinny back until his heat was spent.

He worked harder than she ever had—soaked
his jersey ten minutes in. The boy plunged back
out again the second his father spoke,

and Edna found her unread book slack
on her lap as some gossip blew her way. "I saw
them running together," said the mom who brought snacks

for the team to the mom with the crimson claws.
"They were just too close, you know, no air
between them?" A breeze picked up, random, raw.

Lord, another badly-concealed affair,
with church-pew whisperers assigning blame.
Edna didn't know who they meant, and tried not to hear.

9. ENSORCELLMENTS

Galina was packing up her curly-haired
daughter, a grass-stained sprite sucking so hard
at a juice-box, she ought to pop a shin-guard.

Waiting as her spouse yakked, her boys sparred,
Edna picked up the girl's fairy sweater
and stepped a fateful, toadstool-spotted yard

to hand it over. Jolted, the woman met her
eyes with startled politeness. "Oh, hello,
Edna, thank you." A pause. "I should get her

into a bath, but—" Galina leant in, sotto
voce—"I hear that shrew from Religion threw
a drink at Isabel last night."   "I know,"

Edna found herself saying, scuffing a shoe
against the field as if she meant to leave
a mark, for once. "I was there."   "Were you?"

Galina sparkled now; she almost gave
off beams, Good Witch center-stage. "But why?"
Edna asked, loitering. "I just can't believe

that anyone could be so mad at shy
Isabel." She watched the little goblin-
faced girl devour an astonishing supply

of cheese crackers. Her mother: "Nobody can
understand it. She just won a big
grant for Global Studies, she has the Dean

worshipping her—why should she give a fig
for Isabel? Isabel has nothing."
Edna winced. Galina forced a shrug,

though unresigned. "The High Priestess of Bling,
they call her. Bye!" She darted after a flare
of elf-light—Edna ensnared, the fey girl vanishing.

10. HER FORTITUDE WEAKENS

This is the part, Edna thought in the shower
Monday morning, where I discover a latent
talent: starting mage-fires, maybe. Or,

I get lost among trolls as I try to circumvent
a camp of mercenaries. She lathered her hair,
scratching her scalp, ignoring the impatient

voices that rose through the floor—the daily clamor
of squabbling kids at breakfast. This was the best
ten minutes of the day. Sometimes terror,

sheer as lingerie, was enough to wrest
a gift from the reluctant hero, dragged
clumsily along upon a quest

to save the kingdom. Super-strength, Baggins-
style. Anger can do it. Sometimes, early in
the journey, in a ravine, on the jagged

rocks, he finds his murdered friends eaten
by scavenger crows and the power just
explodes out of him. Rubbing her skin

with a cloth that had begun to stink of must,
Edna sighed. Like what happened to
Bess and Monique? Edna had watched that bust

open, nudged along by a Dean who
ruined love for kicks—well, more fairly,
out of spite at the girl who dared pursue

a formal complaint against him. She had been angry,
worse than now. Edna turned her head in the spray,
out of excuses to linger there. Fury

had not helped anyone, then. Nothing to say
or do, ever. She had no magical power.
She turned off the water, watched it swirl away.

11. THE BARD OPENS A PORTAL

An oil-spill of sorrow stood in Edna's
skull till noon, when Isabel straggled
in like the surf. Although the poet was

almost her own age, Edna struggled
maternally with an urge to wipe her clean.
"Bad weekend?" she asked. Brine-eyed, bedraggled,

Isabel nodded, sat with her coat half-open,
lint-flecked. "That woman who threw her drink at me
at the Jackson Tavern?" The High Priestess of Bling,

Edna thought, but just said, "Yes." A windy
sigh. "I just don't understand what she has against
me. It's like in middle school—she's the bully,

the popular girl, the one with a special sense
for weakness, but why should she even bother? What
threat could I offer?" She laughed at her own expense,

holding her plastic jar of soup to the light.
"Look at this stuff. I can't even pack
a decent lunch." Edna gazed at the white

lumps in muddy broth, the weedy wrack
of faded vegetables. "No, I guess
you can't," she judged. They would swim away from the
    wreck

together. "Hey, why don't you dump that mess
and we'll go out?" Isabel hesitated:
"I teach at one-thirty."   "Isn't that the class

with the stuck-up kids? The class you said you hated?"
Rolled eyes. "Yeah, Advanced Poetry Writing.
I can fake it." She moved to the door, waited

for Edna, full of salt breezes, to grab her things.
"You really should read the pearls I wrote this
weekend. The muse of self-pity! The odes she sings!"

12. Weeks Later, Lost in the Fen

The Women's Studies meeting occurred across
campus, at the low brambly southern end
by the creek. Edna trailed behind the boss—

Galina—and Isabel. She could hardly attend
to their animated fumings. This was the last
event before Thanksgiving break: when

it finished, she could pack up, go home, defrost
some dinner, plan her pies and relishes.
It even smelled of snow. Some brown-streaked grass

flattened under intermittent lashes
of damp wind. The clouds hunched up. The sun quailed.
Into Boggs Hall, past decrepit couches,

down to the basement lounge, dim and stale.
Edna opened up her laptop, ready
to take minutes, and stared around. One frail

classicist had brought her knitting. An eddy
of conversation caught the rest astride
a sofa-boat. Knobby elbows, weedy

hair, wrinkly natural fibers. Edna sighed,
knowing she'd be prisoner for a while.
The colloquy began; bored soggy, she tried

not to take snarky notes. (Gollum-Girl
has caught a grant-fish. Madame Marsh-Wiggle
commends everyone for being cheerful

in the face of disaster.) Man, they could haggle
over the wording of this resolution
for a week. Suddenly, a pall of evil

descended, or a miasma of pollution.
"Sorry I'm late," the Priestess cried, and tossed
her bag on a chair. "How goes the revolution?"

13. THE PRIESTESS AND THE PRIMITIVES

Galina cleared her throat. "We've been asked by the Dean
to collaborate with Global Studies"—here
she gestured at the Priestess and all thirteen

Marsh-Dwellers stiffened, tresses flaring—"on a speaker
for Women's History Month." The silence was so
complete that Edna imagined she could hear

the rushes swishing. One hungry mosquito
whined across the fetid mud. Finally
Isabel said, "There's a poet from Puerto Rico

I've been wanting to bring." A smile widened slowly
on the Priestess's face: she was pleased by the sacrifice.
"Not a *poet*," she answered, happily, scornfully.

"God! Can we *please* not decide to foist
another *poet* on the students? Can we
invite somebody *good*, who's worth the price,

someone whom people actually want to *see*?"
There was a pause as midge-bitten types translated
this comment mentally—had she really

meant…? Isabel shocked to tears. A chair-leg grated
against linoleum as Galina stood up
and the shouting started. Some joined in, some waited

with bulgy eyes. Edna felt like a cup
about to shatter: hot and too full. The aggressor
flounced out after dire warnings. There was a dip

in the talk, a surge again, a drift over
to the covered dishes of roasted roots — the vegan
potluck, unsweetened consolation. Her

mascara streaky, Isabel sat at the sodden
center, enjoying the fuss if not the cuisine.
Edna sidled away from the dismal scene.

14. A Ghost at the Thanksgiving Feast

"Thanks," Edna said ungratefully when
the oyster dressing finally arrived
at her end of the table. None of the sin,

not even a rind of bacon had survived
the journey past her relatives. She scraped
some sage-scented crumbs onto her plate and dived

for mushroom gravy before it too escaped.
Her father and his second wife were angels
in the kitchen, and in fact outstripped

the seraphim in all their charitable toils.
This kindness made Edna feel all the meaner.
Christian love, mission trips, neighborliness—such gospels

did not move her, nor make her like her stepmother
much. Flushing as she thought it, Edna felt
a pat on her velvet sleeve. It was her younger

son, striving to follow the usual adult
discussion about absent kin. She explained
that there were two Georges and Granddad meant

the elder one, and yes, he had been brained
by falling masonry, but that was a long
time ago. He pondered. "So, who am I named

after?"   "Hmm?" Distracted, she raised a prong
of silver, admired the spud, roasted to a turn.
Her boy: "You're named after a poet." A sing-song

quote from Auntie Liz: "'My candle burns
at both ends.'" Edna nodded, mouth full (Liz looked
a little pickled) and buttered rolls for her sons.

Everyone was listening now. The step-cook
suddenly broke. "Don't talk about that woman!"
she bayed and then begged pardon. Her wings shook.

15. The Herbwoman's Lore

"That was a terrible thing for me to say."
Her stepmother wouldn't stop apologizing.
"It was, don't shake your head! And on a holiday,"

she added, rueful, "when you must be thinking
of your mother." There was a natural balm, both hoped,
in homely chores, so each worker did her thing—

ran hot water, readied dish-towels. "I don't read
much, you know, like she did, just magazines,
but I leafed though some poetry when I married

your father—your mother's and that woman
Millay. Your mother's verse was just too tricky
for me, but Millay I understood—all pining

and bitter sophistication. I hated to see
your head in that book, and you just a girl."
Edna didn't even remember the nasty

poems she had supposedly studied, a world
ago, so she kept her tongue and wiped another
piece of china. Squeak, clatter, still.

"Of course you grew up just fine, so your father
was right." This was the longest speech she had made
in years. Edna divined the poor woman's fear

of saying it wrong; though gingerly, she stood
her ground and talked while she had the gumption. "You
married a decent man, you have two good

boys, but sometimes I think you look a little blue."
Edna examined her hands for the unhappy tint
but saw only a chapped, shamed pink. "Value

what you have," she finished in a sprint,
nettled by dirty dishes and revelation.
"And just, well, pray to God if you can't."

16. AFTER DOING DISHES, THE HERO EMBRACES HER DESTINY

Yoda I am, the Voice intoned. "Shut up,"
Edna answered irritably. "What, Mom?"
her elder son asked, yawning. She smoothed the top

of his head. "Talking to myself. Now scram,
to bed, it's late." He clunked his toothbrush in
its mug, dried his face with a sleeve, leaned in for some

love and padded off. "So, where have you been?"
*Stewing roots in my cave, clucking over
your failure to believe in the Force, Foolish One.*

"Everyone wants to convert me." With an angry shiver,
Edna rinsed clots of blue paste from the basin, stretched
for the cord to the blind. The window was a mirror

backed by darkness. *If you're not attached
to the fantasy thing, I could be the demon
on your shoulder. Your stepmother's tale.* "Bewitched,"

Edna muttered, unfurling the shade. *Woman
with magical powers chooses the domestic
lot,* the Voice mused. *The PTA and Lemon*

Pledge. She suddenly sat down on the plastic
toilet-lid. "Nuh-uh," she said. "Not that story.
Not even the secret back-up hope, the sarcastic

princess. I want to be Luke and hog all the glory."
Ambitious you are. It sounded amused. *Now I'm
the skeptic, which is a feat for an imaginary*

mentor. "Get on with it, the cryptic rhyme
about the next step of the quest." Edna felt tense.
Patience, apprentice. Soon it will be time

for a gaudy interlude with the Gyptians.
Listen carefully to their lays. "Some tip,"
she snorted. Wisdom there is in ancient legends.

17. ENTER THE PAINTED CARTS

The hermit Chair, rarely seen outside
his woodland eyrie, stuck his silver head
into the office. "Welcome back!" he cried,

as if Edna had been the missing one, last spotted
lecturing the deer about Thoreau
while hunting for morels upon Mount Dread.

"The external evaluators are here." Although
rusty around their brilliant company,
he was a courtly man. To give the status quo

a lube and tune-up, he occasionally
imported a team of traveling folk to tool
around and write a report—weathered but merry

academics from another school.
He waved them in. "This is Edna, who's
really the one in charge." A colorful

man in scarves came in, another in red shoes,
and they alluded to a woman dawdling
in the ladies' room. A ballad ensues,

predicted Edna, a story encoding a darkling
prophecy—but there was just laughter to start,
hellos all round and shots of coffee. Sing

to me of a magic blade—but they were girt
with disposable pens, their weapons of choice, and seemed
ready for data and meetings, actual work.

Well. Isabel, then, should be poked (she dreamed
her day away without reminders) and the stout
medievalist must be roused from his fastness. She deemed

it the woodsman's job to hunt up the Dragon; he got
hazard pay for such expeditions. She shied
the rest into parley. They sparkled with strangers about.

18. LEGENDS ARE TRUER THAN HISTORY

The next two days were respite in a smoke-
wreathed camp after lonely weeks on the road. Wounds
were dressed with special ointments, worn tales and jokes

traded. They shared hot suppers, splurged on rounds
of spicy ale, and told fortunes. The crabby
professors she worked for seemed almost social—sounds

of cheery conversation burst from shabby
tents, and scholars' sunken cheeks regained
their apple-bright curves. Edna snooped on the gabby

visitors at every chance but obtained
no new intelligence, no cryptic scrap
of information, until the autumn light drained

from her office on the last afternoon. A tap
on the doorframe. It was the old lady. "May
I have a cup of tea?" She clutched a wrap

of crimson wool around her soft shoulders; what day
survived shone on her face. "Of course," Edna said,
and started the kettle, offered good Earl Grey

or oolong, picked out a flowered cup. "You've fed
us well," the visitor said, gratefully warming
her hands on the ceramic. She hesitated

before adding, "I knew your mother a bit," beaming.
Edna spun towards her radiance. The woman
glowed now. "Years ago—she was performing

her poems at my school. She was so determined,
so funny and quick, I admired her so much. I bought
every book." Edna felt the words on her skin

like a nearby blaze. A sip. "You know, you ought
to watch that Dean with Isabel. He stalks
young women of color then he pushes them out."

19. THE HEALER BEGINS AN INCANTATION

"Turns out he ditched his last job because of cases
there," Edna told Monique on the phone that night,
"allegations of quid pro quo. They'd have pressed

charges if he hadn't left at the speed of light."
She could hear Monique's scowl as she said, "We—
I mean the College—prefers to stall. You indict

a sitting dean and it's practically
impossible to hire the next one. Better
to keep everything hushed up, even buy

off the victims, and pass him off to the next sucker."
Mark my words, the old woman had said, Isabel
is in trouble. Edna perched on a chair,

feet drawn up, the room dim; a golden ball
on the tree reflected her in miniature,
and bulbs flashed off and on. The pine had a smell

of wakefulness, a walk in the snow. "I saw Her,"
Monique disclosed in a different voice. "Pretend
Christmas spirit. We talked at a party." This scared

Edna. The break-up with Bess had destroyed her friend.
"No, I'm okay, it was fine. I'm just worried,
Bess working for that predator." Edna couldn't stand

to look at Bess anymore, but had heard
that she was miserable, that after wooing
Bess for the job, the Dean had her interred

in a shallow grave of spreadsheets. "No more stewing
over her, you promised," Edna warned, picking lint
from her snowman socks. "You know that's not what
   I'm doing.

Just—would you check up on her?" Edna didn't
promise, but she still stayed up thinking of Bess.
The colored lights blinked, blithely inconsistent.

20. THE MERCENARY CHANGES ALLEGIANCE

The whole town hibernated the week
between New Year's Day and the students' return—except
for those who had vowed to sweat off a larded physique,

walking in twos and threes, all chapped and windswept.
Since resolve had kindled in her gut,
Edna didn't feel the cold, hardly slept.

She peeled off her gloves en route to the restaurant,
about to meet Bess, all jittery. Hello,
hello, she said to each bear on its jaunt,

mast-stuffed friends of her parents, their noses aglow.
A little bell jingled, and everybody shook
in the breeze when she opened the door to the bistro.

Bess sat by the window and waved. She did look
haggard. When Edna began with pleasantries,
Bess brushed them off. "You know I work for a jerk,"

she blurted. "The burger, medium rare, please.
Either he doesn't tell me enough for me
to do my job, and I look stupid—no cheese—

or he leans on me so hard—oh, god, there he
goes." They peered through the glass together. Most
of the administrators, and a few faculty

on the fast track, ran together at lunch. The first
in the pack was the Dean, and the Priestess panted just
behind him, struggling to keep up. Too close.

Edna suddenly remembered that gust
of soccer gossip. Running together, no space
between them... Bess smirked at her. "You've got the gist."

"That's why the Priestess is so smug!" The plates
came. "And also why she's freaked. But Monique—"
Bess interjected. "She's why we're on this date."

21. CASTLE BUILDERS

"I know how badly I screwed that up," Bess
admitted and begged Edna for information—
was Monique seeing someone, might she say yes

to another try? Meanwhile Edna's portion
of potato-leek soup cooled as she pried out details
about the Dean's affair. Before the foundation

of Global Studies, or after? No one else
had figured things out yet, and Bess expected he would
keep it secret-while the Priestess held on with her nails

and Nikes. "She thinks she's well along the road,
but he'll drop that portcullis so fast—" Edna jumped.
"What? Oh." Bess snorted between great chomps of food.

"I'm all, like, gothic since Monique," and she slumped.
"Anyway, everything's power for him, and she
doesn't have enough, she'll get dumped.

The treacherous king always has some crafty
plan—a secret passage behind a painting,
stiletto up his sleeve." By the time she finished her coffee,

a bolder Bess had peeked behind some hangings,
tapped the walls until the echo sounded
auspicious. Edna stumbled home past the panting

dogs and their weary walkers. She was confounded
by blueprints, siege plans, visions of axes and dire
new tools of rebellion. He was surely surrounded

by people—women, at least—who wanted the empire
to crumble already. Even his Mercenary
was disenchanted, honing her scimitar

against her former Lord, donning her scary
leather pants. The battlements a mess,
flags torn. The vultures circling, greedy, wary.

22. MARTIAL BALLADS

Isabel jingled in one morning and croaked,
"Did you hear about the faculty meeting?" These
occurred in the late afternoons, so the staff ducked

out early. "The Dean speaks for Courses and Degrees,
right, and you know how he's never prepared, and how
he takes forever, and everyone just agrees

to his proposals so he'll shut up?" Her brow
was creased with urgent lines—sheet music, Edna
thought. "I don't even know what it was about,

I wasn't following," the poet confessed. "He said the
word 'interdisciplinary' and I zoned.
Well, Galina stood up, dressed to the hilt, and read a

statement about how the Dean had undermined
existing programs in favor of his hobby horse.
I mean, some of the old guard just groaned,"

she allowed, "because it was Galina, those morons,
but she's totally right." She told of a battle complete
with flying spells, quickly marshaled force,

and peasants with pitchforks; repeated a speech
about the resemblance of incompetence
to malice; and sang of the Dean's shamed retreat.

Not a likely finale. On the pretense
she had forms for Galina to sign, Edna left
the office after the bard and turned right. Suspense

prickled her neck. Sure enough, a soft
tune of voices, bass and treble, unrolled
from the cracked door. Edna strained for the drift.

"That monologue will cost you," the Dean told
Galina, plucking a low string. "Your program is fucked."
I know this song, thought Edna. This one's old.

23. A GLIMPSE OF THE DARK LORD

The tyrant swept by in a sulfurous mist. She shrank
against a ratty poster of William Shakespeare
on the wall, but the Dean didn't notice, thank

goodness. Her tendency to disappear
was a gift after all. She gulped and touched
her mother's ring as she watched him veer

around the corner. People admired his notched
smile, those tumbling inky locks—they said
he was rakishly handsome. They had been bewitched,

Galina countered, by his Ivy-League cred
and trendy jargon. Monique declared that his height
helped him—that was how people wanted

their leaders to look, virile, looming. The sight
of him made her feel small, Edna admitted, but
she thought his basso, profound as a snowy night,

froze everyone. She straightened, resolute,
shook off the cold, and listened again. A pause
as Galina second-guessed herself. Too astute

to believe his curse, but unsure of her own powers,
she would be alarmed now. Yes, there was the call
Edna expected to hear. She started to pass

down the corridor, letting Galina tell
of the visit in a dozen urgent phone
appeals, talking her way from distress to moral

righteousness, but then stopped to look at her own
ghost face in the window glass, framed between
Langston Hughes and Sylvia Plath. Alone,

each figure, except for the voices. Onto the scene
in the Dragon's lair, just another door down. *I think
it's time*, she told Yoda, *a message I bring.*

24. ROUSING THE ANCIENT LIZARD

She knocked three times on the office door. Peace,
at first, like a meadow on a high mountain, dotted
with tiny scented blossoms. Then a faint wheeze

from deep in the rock. Edna listened, waited.
Someone was pondering the summons, curious,
annoyed. Another rustle. The recluse snorted.

"Well, come in," she said, clearly furious
with herself for needing to know who dared
disturb her. A blink. "Why, Edna, yes.

How have you been, dear?" The Dragon stared
with small bright eyes at this person from Porlock, but
she was kind as well as fierce, her eye-teeth bared

in a genuine smile. She had loved Edna's mother. "What
beautiful jewelry," the hero answered, gazing
at the professor's gorgeous gems. "I bought

these in Oxford," the scholar said, preening. Praising
the dragonish display of silks and gold
was ceremonial. "Now," she said, with amazing

acuity, "Sit down. I am not so old
and beastly that I cannot see your burden.
What has happened?" The daughter sat and told

her, a little hypnotized by the gleam of verdant
satin, by alpine fragrance. Her auditor
was not shocked, though perhaps her scales hardened

a little. "You have done rightly. I will record
what you have said, and I will contemplate
the best way to proceed. This dean is a bully and a boor" —

Edna imagined a tail-tip twitching — "but a threat
overheard by you may not yet be enough." These
stupid men, said her eyes, so good to eat.

25. An Unexpected Ally

Edna walked slowly down the stairs toward
the central office, brooding. For a dragon,
especially one with a satisfying hoard,

a human lifetime wasn't very long.
And it's hard to rewrite a well-known story. She
passed the poet's door on the way to her own and then

doubled back. Isabel sat there, shivery,
eyes round. "What's up?" Edna demanded. "You
look worried."   "The Dean stopped by." Misery,

despair, as if a blizzard had whirled through
the building. "He came in and put his hands on the back
of my chair while he talked, so he had a perfect view

of my screen but I couldn't see him." Hauling a stack
of essays, the Chair creaked through and stopped as well.
"I saw the Dean leave," he boomed. The woodsman
      could track

a stray thought as surely as a herd of gazelle
on the rampage, but he seldom chose to. It was weird
for him to even pause and talk. "What the hell

did *he* want?" And what in heaven had roused Gray-Beard
from his hermit oblivion? "He wanted to check
how my writing was going." Isabel had teared

up already. "He said that since my teaching is weak
and I have no publisher, that he's concerned
about my next review, and could we speak

in his office sometime soon." The woodsman burned
on the inside; Edna could smell it. "The department
    stands
behind you, Isabel. He spoke out of turn.

Don't go see him—I will," her defender ground
out and strode away stiffly. Now that's a sword
you rarely see—aflame in a woodsman's hand.

26. ALWAYS WINTER AND NEVER CHRISTMAS

"But battles are ugly when women fight," she read
aloud, and cried, "Ugh!" Both boys giggled, though
used to their mother's wrinkled nose. "Repressed

that part." Edna did recall a thaw
and Father Christmas with the teapot, all much
nicer. This book was impossible, so sweet, so

noxious. Edna finished the chapter and touched
her eldest boy's head—he no longer tolerated
kisses—and chased the little one across

the hall to his own room, which was decorated
with toy weapons. "I am Queen Susan!" she shouted,
"Fear my dreadful bow!" When the squeals abated,

she walked around closing shades. She doubted
spring would ever come. This winter, once white,
had lengthened into gray. Once crocus sprouted,

deceived by a false spring, but an icy night
had obliterated them. Nothing ever
happened, and no one slipped her Turkish Delight

to take her mind off frozen fauns. A fever
of work consumed Isabel, and her colleagues hid
likewise in their solitary lairs.

Monique and Bess had met, had talked, had
not found a path forward. Galina threw
out curses — the Women's Studies budget did

get slashed ("declining interest") while the new
program in Global Studies expanded. "Study
these globes," Galina hissed backstage, a claw

on each round breast. When things promised to get bloody,
though, the thermometer would dip instead.
But tomorrow is March, she thought. Time to get muddy.

27. AVATAR OF A GODDESS

Edna left the Commons with a wrap
for lunch; Galina had been there, gathering
signatures for a petition. On up

the hill, she noticed Isabel shuddering
under a winter-blighted tree and the Dean
speaking to her in those deep tones, smothering

her with little touches—intimate gestures that mean
nothing among friends, two fingers to the arm,
a hand on the elbow. The Priestess entered the scene,

apparently leaving class, and stopped in alarm
when she saw them. She flushed blood-dark as Kali,
ready to stomp Shiva's breast, all rage to his charm,

then the incarnation faded. She slumped sadly,
adjusted her necklace of skulls, and slipped into
the Religion building. One almost felt sorry

for her. Bess walked up then and shared Edna's view
of the tête-á-tête under the oak. "Someone
has to do something," Edna said. "You do,"

Bess replied, and in response to the frown,
continued, ticking off fingers. "Monique did try,
but it was he-said-she-said, then she was gone.

I filed a complaint a month ago, just my
problems, and they said I was the first complainant,
and that I couldn't expect them to fire the poor guy

when he didn't mean any harm. A shame to ruin
his whole life over a mistake or two.
And Isabel's untenured." Bess's grin

was full of daggers. "So am I!" A cloud blew
over the weak sun. Edna moved a step
out of the wind. "But Edna, they can't fire *you*."

28. THE FINAL CONFRONTATION

"I'd like to report some problems with the Dean,"
Edna said, her lunch spoiling in her purse.
It had seemed unwise to wait, to risk cooling down,

so she had marched right up to the Provost's office,
past her great-grandfather's portrait—he looked
like a lion stuffed with sawdust. A book of verse

by Edna's mother glimmered from the ranked
talismans of faculty distinction
arranged across the shelves. Edna had thanked

the Provost for these moments of attention,
without an appointment; in fact, it had been hard
to weasel past the sentry at reception.

The frail old man had problems with his heart
and everyone protected him. Our hero
did not. She started with how the Dean would hound

Isabel; that information had zero
effect on the Provost's herbivore smile, but news
of his threat to Galina and the subsequent blow

to her budget made him focus that wandering blue
gaze. The pièce de résistance was the affair
with the Priestess—"common knowledge," which
    was untrue,

though it wasn't as secret as some parties desired. She stared
at the Provost and he glared back. "All this is second-
hand," he said, "or worse, so I am required

to investigate the facts." At that, she reckoned
he knew them already, had preferred to ignore them,
    and now
was angrily trapped. He would rather gnaw his own

leg off than break the snare. She left with a bow
to her oily ancestor, his mutton-chops bristling, his dun
wool too snug by far. Hunger deepened his scowl.

29. ANTICLIMAX

Edna daydreamed at her desk, her window
cracked so she could smell the lawn greening
up again. As her cell-phone rang, a low

voice nudged her: *The next revolution means answering*
yes. "Be quiet," she replied. "Hello?" Monique's
daily call to check on her without seeming

to be worried—she thought Edna seemed wan. Six weeks
since she'd dared the Provost's den. Not much
of an ultimate battle, really. No gore, no shrieks

of wounded avian minions. If she'd set a match
to the tower, it had yet to catch, though Bess insisted
a few things had changed. The Dark Lord didn't mooch

around Isabel now. And he noticed that Edna existed.
Everybody did, as if all the light
that had bent around her once suddenly twisted

to blaze on her winter-pale face. As if of late
an old enchantment had been lifted. As if
the College had not kept her risky complaint

confidential. Well, at least a whiff
of spring had penetrated the building. The chair
had brought her a fist of daffodils as a gift

from the inscrutable woods; they nodded at her
from a jar. *The Final Confrontation*
is never what you expect, my Adept. Beware

the Dwarf's handiwork. Then, a manifestation:
the medievalist asking for copies. She pretended
not to mind. The machine had constipation—

every paper Edna fed it offended
its innards. It groused; she groused. Then, aglow
with triumph, Isabel burst in. "The siege has ended!"

30. TRANSFIGURATION

"My book has been accepted!" Isabel crowed.
She hopped around the office waving her contract,
a fan of scribbled feathers; happiness showed

in the shine of her eyes, her body's ease, the distracted
way she unclipped and loosened her hair—a bird
on the highest tree-branch, fearless. Edna attacked

her with hugs, Galina too, having wandered, bored,
past the door and heard the warbling. "I knew
it!" Galina shouted. "I didn't," answered the bard.

"Even when the publisher's message came through,
asking if the manuscript was available,
I didn't believe it was real." She removed one shoe,

then the other; they were lofty and purple,
and without them she looked even more wren-boned,
small enough to fly. "I was sure there'd be trouble."

"Why?" Edna demanded. Isabel cocked her head.
"I just didn't think I was that kind of person." Her cronies
waited. "The kind of person who got what she wanted."

Galina roared some obscenity. Edna's
response, though, was wistful. "I understand."
But Isabel had broken all those laws.

Eventually, with her cast-off heels in one hand,
the poet left to call her mother. The Witch,
as Edna now deemed her, left too. When Edna turned

to shut down, though, her cell trilled again. *Don't switch
your computer off,* read the text from Gnomic Utterance.
She looked at her screen. Her skeptical mouse-finger
    twitched.

Nothing. A breeze full of April scents.
Then, yes, a mass email message glowed
there. From the void, words: "Unexpected Events."

31. THE DARK LORD FLEES

"On behalf of the President of the College"—blah, blah,
"I regret to announce that the Dean has accepted
an equal-rank job at Similar U, far, far

away, in a hip city. We are all indebted
to him for his service, especially his commitment
to international initiatives," et

cetera. Could this be another figment
of Edna's warped imagination? The timing
seemed real; they preferred to shake the firmament

at four-thirty on a spring Friday, so the whining
would be brief and half-hearted. However, the next
    paragraph
was almost too sweet to believe: Bess would be signing

on as Acting Dean. Monique must have laughed—
and sobered up quickly. Getting Bess through next year
would require all the Healer's uncanny craft.

Now, power down. Time to disappear.
She touched the talisman she wore on a chain
and looked deep into the dead monitor's mirror.

That visage was like her mother's, but for the chin,
and the curls all wrong. Hers was the voice Edna'd
    longed
to hear. Hers was the hallowed apparition

Edna waited for. Hopeful, she prolonged
the moment, but heard only the sigh of light in decline,
saw only how every mother's ghost belonged

in every daughter's face, what passed for divine
visitation these days. Resemblance
and echo would have to be enough. Resigned,

The One of Several stood up by the window. Her trance
broke when she saw the Dragon on the lawn,
chortling with the woodsman. Giddy—no pretense.

32. CONTEMPLATING THE SEQUEL

Sunshine buzzed through the curtains and voices gleamed
through the cracked door—the noises boys make when
   they play
alone, action-figure trash-talk, the low scream

of a raider blasting off. Edna lay
awake thinking, *I never found my star-metal
sword or a book of runes, or fought my way*

*through a grove of sentient trees, or delivered my tale
to the northern horsemen over a smoky fire,
hoping to recruit a few for my team*—until

she realized that her husband was looking at her
happily. "Good morning," she said, and clasped his rough
hand. After a while she spoke again. "The letter

from Financial Aid came yesterday. It's enough."
She lifted her head a bit, searched his eyes
for a word, and discovered, *Yes.* A sniff.

She was tearing up, to her own surprise.
"I'm scared," she said. He hugged her. "Think of the worst
students you've signed forms for at the College—
   if those guys

can earn degrees, you'll rock the universe."
She persisted: "It'll be hard for you and the kids,
me studying every weekend, getting stressed

about exams, commuting upstate." He kissed
her. "You deserve a new arena. The secretary
thing was convenient, but I knew it wouldn't last."

"And that's okay?" He sat up and stared.
"You know I'm proud of you, right, how you stuck
it to The Man? You had a crazy year,

but you helped fix that place." She felt herself relax,
suddenly, deeply. "So what's your next grand scheme,
superstar?" She smiled. "A major in Politics."

33. HAVING SAVED THE WORLD

"What do Politics majors do when they
grow up?" asked Thing One. Thing Two, jumping
on the bed, sent the cat skidding. He shouted, "They slay

dragons!"   "Never," Edna admonished, thumping
him on the leg with a paperback. "Here, look
at this one." He peered at *Ronia* before dumping

it with the other discards. "No books
with girls on the covers." She huffed and said to her eldest,
"Sometimes they become lawyers," then shook

a fatter book at Thing Two, trying to interest
him in its picture. "This one has orange fire,
plus a griffin." He sat down promptly for a rest.

"And knights with crossbows. But lawyer sounds like liar,"
he observed. *He looks like my mother—those cheekbones,
enormous eyes.* She patted her lap to lure

him over and started to read from Diana Wynne Jones:
"Mr. Chesney won't let women do
the Dark Lord." She spoke in different tones

and accents, although she didn't know who
each character would turn out to be, not yet.
The voices were hers and every one was true.

(Sometimes the Voice still lectured in her head,
but it was different now, not quite a sound—
just language winging through as if it forgets

where it woke up that morning, can't tell where it's bound.)
Both boys settled in, as they did when a good tale
caught them up, mouths slack, absorption profound.

She forgot herself, too, didn't notice her tall
son twisting her curls, the bedroom's disarray.
Transformed by haunted words. That miracle.

II
Other Tales

THE HORROR AT FOX HOLLOW

Fur prickled, pulse in a stutter, Kit turns off
   the highway onto country roads. The woods
   gleam between the fields—each gap a soft
unsettled mood shaped by walls that have stood,
   stone-faced, for hoary decades. From time to time
   she slows to squint at her notes by dash-light. Good
that she's alone. Her husband and son would team
   up to tease her for resisting GPS.
   But she won't get lost: Kit has print. Her beams
pick out the signs—and a sly possum, and a mess
   of dead doe gnawed by a shape that scurries away—
   so she follows her lines to Fox Hollow School for Girls.
An avenue of trees. Each raises a splay
   of dead fingers where blossoms should be. A guard
   in a bright-lit hut, clean-shirted, scribble of gray
combed over his scalp, limps out. "Katherine Rennard,"
   she tells him, "here for the Poetry Festival."
   He steps back, rings someone, then waves her forward.
Belated panic thrills her. She could roll
   up her window, hang a quick K-turn, and go.
   A reading for two hundred teens? Too brutal.
But now she's trapped. There, under the glow
   of security lights, waits the spunky teacher,
   scarlet with enthusiasm for his not-too-
famous poet: tomorrow's special feature.
   Tonight, just listening. She's come mid-event,
   the Student Slam, and ducks into the bleachers.

No one heeds her; their whispery heads are bent
   together, in rows, at tables, in the furtive
   poses plotters take when poised to torment
their sisters. It's a secret. Don't want to hurt
   your feelings but. My god what is she wearing.
   Not aimed at Kit, but it's easy to revert—
sneer down at her own wrinkled self, her timid bearing.
   Still the odd one. Masked. Teacher's pet.
   It's not a true slam, no one scruffy or swearing,
but all are keen, straining the leash. That edge.
   Two half-grown, trembling girls, their meter poor,
   recite a piece together, giggling, and get
off the stage before they hear the abysmal score.
   Someone still in riding breeches shakes
   her auburn tresses and declaims a more
successful paean to her horse. She likes
   to wring the cheers from slender throats. The winner,
   toothy, bites off an ode to midnight snacks.
The scene is gothic. Kit knows this tale of horror:
   a stranger comes to town. Folks seem normal—
   too normal. She suppresses an improper snicker.
As it ends, a meager fog descends, miasmal.
   Kit's brought to a vacant guesthouse for the night.
   It's an ancient pile. The rooms are queer and dismal.
She nudges the doorstop aside—a crouched thing, not
   quite canine, made of metal—unzips her bag,
   hangs up her reading outfit, finds a note
from her son, tries to phone. Reception's bad,
   so the nature-poet draws her blinds against
   the mumbling trees, the silent huddled birds.
There's an oval portrait on her wall amidst
   the paper's tangled ivy: the mug of a fox,
   wary, studying some long-dead artist.

Kit finally dozes after testing the locks.
    Do the dreams bring on the fear or does the fear
    bring on the dreams? *A forest clearing. The clock's*
insect tick. She and her poetry books premiere
    on a low stage, fixed in the spotlight. She knows
    the risers are stocked with voyeurs. They leer at her
till dawn, when she rinses off the helplessness
    and hears her host's horn sound. The handles on
    his car are useless from the inside. "That noise,"
Kit asks. "Is it dogs?"   "The baying of the hounds,"
    he gamely replies. "During these winter weeks
    the girls just love a fox-hunt." He parks, walks round
to let her out. "Don't worry, they're sated," he jokes.
    The earth is pocked and fragrant, deeply scored
    by hoof and pad and other illegible tracks.
The master leads her on a walking tour
    of campus—a moss-veiled dorm, a spiffy gym
    for that twenty-first-century tone—and recounts
        some lore
of miscellaneous hauntings. Best, in the grim
    cafeteria, he gestures to a portrait of
    the founder, vigorous and slim,
a coil of ghostly smoke floating above
    her hand, though her brandy and lit cigarette
    are painted out. Finally, at a remove
from the other buildings, the venue. And wild regret,
    as always, that she's agreed to this. Either way,
    whether the reading's triumphant or painful, Kit
will feel chagrin. There's something about a stage
    that alienates a person from herself.
    As if, she thinks as she dog-ears some pages,
half-attending to the introductory riff,
    I'm not just the fox but the pack of hounds, too.
    And it's time for the beasts to be cast into the rough.

She wonders what she'll see from the lectern—a few
    well-mounted, vicarious hunters, checking her over?
    Or slavering fangs? By instinct, she leaps at her cue.

—Here the fragment ends; the contriver
    of these verses left them unfinished, unsigned.
    I return the scrap of foolscap to its clever
covert: a frayed edition left behind
    by some other traveler. In the middle
    of a journey, lost in a wood, the Fox Hollow kind.
Lovecraft would find "a hideous cult of nocturnal
    worshipers…a revolting fertility-rite."
    Intense seclusion can make a visitor smell
like lunch. But then, I can be Kittish. A night
    with no hounds is bad enough. A prep-
    school is always grounds for dread: those bright
young flames when I'm halfway to ash; their up-
    wardly mobile predation; the descent
    into girl-world. Where my courage slips
and I surrender, though, is in the event.
    That servile play at status. My will and its teeth.
    And no one real—just ambience and scent.
Look up at the window, and there she is, past death,
    translated, a monstrous shimmer in the pane
    where my reflection should be. Flushed out. Both
our mouths ajar. And then, her revenant grin:
    no gap now between think and say, want and eat.
    Devoured, she's whole. And listening for her kin.

Bicameral Woman

Sometimes I draft similes for writing instead of writing.[1]
Alternately, I forage for brainfood.[2] Yesterday I was
reading about a book by Julian Jaynes on the origin of
human consciousness; he has a theory about why people
hear voices, and the book I am not writing concerns
poetic voice. Jaynes, a biologist, argues for a prehistoric
creature he calls "bicameral man" split into an executive
part and a follower. Even in the present day, he theorizes,
the left-brain speech center controls our conversation,
while the apparently dormant right-brain speech center
offers advice in stressful periods through auditory
hallucinations.[3] *Time!* I check my watch, slam down the
book, lope off to pick up my children. While we catch
our breath and graze,[4] we talk about my third-grade
daughter's invisible friends, a dinosaur and a monster who
began visiting when she was two.[5] I am surprised to learn

1   Writing a scholarly book is like climbing a mountain in flippers.
2   There are no chocolate-orange biscotti in my sabbatical office.
    I look down from a modular building through a twin-boled oak
    at a wooded trail. A hidden creek occasionally sends emissary
    dragonflies to bump against my window.
3   Before Grandfather Ape was quite conscious—when he could
    talk a little but was not able to exercise abstract thought and
    remember what he wanted from the creek an hour ago—he
    might have wandered out to the rocky edge of the water and
    looked around foolishly. At that point the right brain would
    issue a verbal hallucination: "Mmm, cress, good with mammoth
    cutlets, Grandmother might have sex with you if you bring this
    home."Grandfather thinks he is hearing the river god.
4   Havarti and plums.
5   Her invisible friend dinosaur was named "Friend Dinosaur" and her
    invisible friend monster was named "Friend Monster."

that she still hears from them. She "pretended" to take them to school in her hair last year and "pretended" they gave her answers to tests. She rarely sees them anymore now that she is so old, and they do not come when she calls, but sometimes she can feel their presence.[6] When she describes the sensation she taps the right side of her head.[7]

---

6   Sometimes I seize words from the water, one at a time with dreadful effort, and the slippery fish taste terrible. Sometimes they leap up from darkness, delicious.

7   I should just perch on the river rocks in big wet dirty flippers and breathe thin air. The gods might tell me what to eat. Or maybe they wouldn't. It's hard to tell the difference.

Just Long Enough to Hurt

Grooves of ivy twisted along the silver
rims, and some demon haunted the lenses—
a spirit, a desire. When she raised the glasses
to her face, she felt it stir. Through their frames
she glimpsed the real world, not this shadow
place with its sagging wires and dirty streets,
but skies she knew, where bronze-tipped clouds cast
patterns of *yes* and *no* over the pastures.
Scared, she mislaid the spectacles time and again.

Wanting hurts—so she tolerates blurry
contours, buys a car, eats from plastic
packages. Just once in a while, for a minute,
she puts on windows, hazards everything.
Lids wide, she hears each separate shaft of grass,
freely bent and humming its allegiance
to the wind. Closer by, hunger buzzes,
a wasp in her hair. The living metal crackles.
A glimpse. Just long enough to say *yes*, and *no*.

THE BOOK OF NEUROTRANSMITTERS

The heaviest book in the library basement is stripped of gilt
by all those fingers whispering around its edges. One must
handle it to learn its name. *Open me, open me,* it says —
finishing, as one splays the leaves, *and you will regret
it forever.*

                Dear Necronomicon, when I dream now
I rehearse the birth-pains of the human world, our battles
with original monsters, the fires that burned so long.
Your formulas scribble themselves across my vision
like a migraine. Your tables, ideographs, obscene
incantations have rewritten the chemical messages
my cells transmit, and I seem to be printed with gibberish,
degraded codes. I know how to raise the dead from their salts
but cannot get out of bed. The doctors' scripts — oh plain
illegibility! — flutter down, washed into the gutter by autumn
storms. I fear that if I rise again I will leave a slug's
silver trail to the regions you describe, and that trail will be
    a map,
and some innocent soul will read it and betray herself
    thereby.

Not a Metaphor But a Lifestyle

A cough-drop spaceship tracks him everywhere,
whining some complaint into his ear.
Its flicker winks when people glance over.

A figment, they think. Still the metallic buzz
persists, a fine drill boring in.
He was nine when it began. Missing

his soldier-father. At first it smelled
like medicine, a high-tech promise
that pain will disappear. Its signal fuzzed

out nightmares. Kept him company. Then
its insect cry sharpened and herded
him from friends. He saw their mouths shape

words but could not hear what they meant.
Permanent wrinkles grooved his brow. He
started to hunch against the hornet's song,

maddened by a sting that never came.
No thread of light widening small doors.
No one to say what the static means.

Rumpelstiltsken

[before]

Ruth's a fine name, he argues, *but Evelyn's the queen*
of grandmas — she hangs up without saying goodbye.
The leaves quibble and his pregnant wife shrugs.

Her silence wobbles the hot brine in her belly
and the fetus wakes, removes a pleasantly fat and
    salty thumb
from her mouth, and gazes up through red-lit membranes.

[now]

Some smiling adult places the cordless phone to her ear.
It's the sea in a shell: a grandmother's voice through a veil
of golden hair, through space, broken into data and rebuilt

into presence. She doesn't believe it's her nana without
    the smoky
waft of coffee, a soft body pushing air through those words.
She doesn't believe they *are* words. *Yes*, she says. *Yes, yes, bye.*

[once upon a time]

The woman who made a promise sends messengers into the woods.
The first day, they just sit on a stump and eat cheese.
Returning, they lamely offer their queen: Tom, Dick, Harry.

You've heard this story before. Shortribs, Sheepshanks—
other bad-luck monikers not in your name book.
On the third day, one discovers a little man gloating over his bet.

[someday]

Ruthie Evelyn Miller King dabs on some kiwi lip-gloss.
Her best friend has just earned her license and
   they're driving
to a party in the county. The radio plays a tune

we can't imagine yet, and they sing along.
It's a hot wet night. A cute boy with curly hair
   is awkwardly
quiet. She dares him: *Bet you can't guess my name.*

Villainous Creeds

Hook

I fret, as Eton's Captains do, about good
form. Pirates must cut a figure even though Pan
out-masters every seaman—surely God
prefers that lawless boy, guards him from pain,
cherishes even his baby fangs. I will dream
of them when I have been devoured, my dapper
prosthesis rusted, compass lost, best rum
tippled by fairies. It will hardly matter
that I sharpened my lapels every night,
ironed my boots, polished my mustaches.
Yet somehow, it does. I still believe in neat
cuffs round bloody hands. Painstaking stitches
for hideous wounds. This is my one power:
to keep my motives small, my heart impure.

The White Witch

Turkish Delight is useful on sleigh rides.
White-garbed patricians are not skilled with children.
Do not neglect the statuary. All roads,
especially those that climb to thrones, run
through a well-equipped wardrobe. These tips
and more at bargain prices in my book—
call this number now. Do not think I stoop
here to mere Christian commerce or balk
at parley with minions: I am a teacher.
I once was cold and ran with wolves, I confess,
but now I desire a legacy. Torture
is a fading art. My golden foe confuses
you. Learn that he is the misanthropic
metaphor, not I. Study my biopic.

George W. Bush

When I am angry, gosh, my homilies
spread freedom and democracy: be clear
that I hear your vision of faith-based families
killing at the whim of a hat. I stand for
things, lots of things. When I have to declare
war, though, I'm prone to stammer. Most times I'm
scared of folks. Justice ought to be fair
and I'll beat those terrorists, but when in Rome
you pray with the Pope and become a dull
boy. Fear makes me tired, is what I'm saying,
and wooly on the details. I can't deal
with your disappointment, the ensuing
big sky silence. If only God didn't
appoint me to serve as your president.

God

I am divinely distant sometimes, and cool
as a figment. Being a great patriarch
in heaven, I neglect to return your call,
gossip about you with my angels, shirk
conflict though I've caused it. You'll never know
whether I love, pity, forget, or despise
you, and our last supper will always gnaw
your conscience with what-ifs. I need my space,
I have earned the right to insist, and you won't
ever be sure what lives behind the door.
Get used to it. Pray, worship all you want,
sacrifice a virgin. Your fix is dire:
yes, your parents helped to cook your head,
but I am the best bad idea you ever had.

ZOMBIE THANKSGIVING

I.   That Corpse You Planted Last Year
          in Your Garden

November surprised us, Congress undone again,
whiff of dread in a drift of mothballed coats.
When we were children, we didn't know we'd always
be children, that the sun would stoop every
year, suddenly reddening a crowd of houses.
Inside ours, mannequins sneered at unwary
looters and the putrid hordes closed in.
Yet when we sat up late instead of packing,
cat on your thighs, iridescent pixels
mirrored in our glasses of beer, I could not
pull the plug. Neither asleep nor awake
but cozy with horror.
Oed' und leer das TV.

Pittsburgh, unreal. I read for much of the drive
through the resentful Alleghenies.
Monsters crawl through the pentameter
of George Romero's *Waste Land.*

Enmities buried last year in drifts
of wrapping paper, will they shrug off their ribbons?
The Monroeville Mall locks its doors with a snick
on the stroke of nine. Keep the undead hence,
whose gas-guzzlers veer from lane to lane.
Hypocrite reader trapped in the refrain.

II.   Hurry up please its time

Scene. A Pontiac ascends the cracked
asphalt roads north of the city, Barbra
and Johnny bickering over an annual rite:
laying a wreath on an old man's grave. Stripped
oaks advise detachment. The radio stutters
apologies. They park, find the stone, where she
kneels and he mocks her respect. Cypress branches
finger his shoulders as the would-be cynic
reminisces. "They're coming to get you, Barbra,"
he taunts, but when Raccoon-Eyed Man attacks,
he protects her. She lurks nearby, ruthless
in her alice band and belted trenchcoat,
observing how Johnny falls. Soon she will sprint
for the car, kicking off treacherous heels,
slipping in mud's confusion. She will release
the emergency break, slide downhill toward
the farmhouse. There is always a farmhouse where
survivors gather to fend off hungry ghouls.
A claustrophobic place. The phone lines dead.
Prejudice condensing in a fog.
You'd think she'd be the one to endure, but
Barbra's carried off before the credits.

Inside the minivan my family
ponders the epidemiology
of zombie apocalypse.
                        He explains, "It's a plague."

I rest my cheek on the window, practicing cold.
They do not know enough to do the same.

"The sick are hard to neutralize, and the well
just keep turning, increasing the infected
population."

I remember mercury

falling. That shimmer gone digital.

A child asks, "What starts it?"
                              "Radioactive germs
from space. Or an experimental virus
engineered in a lab, set free by animal rights
activists. The enemy changes around."

Mercury shrinks in me. I have seen this carnage
before, can taste it now: synthetic gore
of Bosco, hambones. Offense beats quarantine,
but either way decency is doomed.

    III.   Z-Day

Begins with gratitude, everyone pleased to have
    safely steered
through highways clogged with sluggish
    truckers. Embraces,
exclamations over a new haircut or sprouting kid.
Unloading of burdens. Survivors of the first wave
pooling their pies and covered casseroles, cracking open
microbrews. Someone pulls the drapes against the dark.

One in-law hunches quietly near the potato chips,
    his face just
a tinge gray, sheen of perspiration on his cheeks.
He has rolled his holiday sweater sleeve over the
    bite-marks.
Some kid in the rest-stop men's room. Barely broke
    the skin.
His loving wife suspects, but she will never turn him in.

Litter of brimming dishes washes up on the
    table, cranberries
poisonously red, butter chill in its porcelain box.
One grown daughter pours a second glass of wine.
    So thirsty.
Her girl pinches a toddler. Sweet potatoes singe
    and smoke.
The oldest son berates his sister as she scatters pecans
in the salad. "You know Karen is allergic."   "No, it's fine,
it's really all right," Karen cries, panicked she might be
    the trigger.
Everyone knows how tension builds. Grandkids sit at
    the end,
refusing food. Teenagers sneer at their toasted parents.
    The ashen
man lurks as far from them as he can and salts his
    meal before
he tastes it. Every neuron's under siege; fever steams
open his seals. "Oh, the turkey came out dry, what
    a shame,"
he smirks. Grandma wilts. Grandpa stiffens, demands,
"So, son, you still unemployed?" Mortification,
    bluster, rage.
The words seem small, insidious as germs, but they
    can lodge
in anyone. To save your kin, back slowly out of range.

I foresuffered all: bright bow
of insult nocked; bead of tainted
blood swelling after the arrow;
feeble dabbing instead
of confrontation; news
left on, announcer's voice
chiming into our silence

about a wreck or demonstration;
racist joke, napkin tossed down,
plate abandoned; toxic uncle
gone berserk and chewing on a cousin.
Hunkered down, shutting monsters outside,
unearthing more within.

IV.   No More Room in Hell

The zombie in hot pants, a fortnight dead,
forgot the cry of the register, and how to tell the cost
    of things,
and the names of her friends.
                                    A necktied zombie
snacked on her with relish. As they rose and rose
again, they swatted at zombies in turbans or baggy jeans
staggering through the food court.
                                    Cult fan or critic,
O you who scramble into the beating copter,
consider Hot Pants Zombie, who once was tender-hearted too.

V.   What the Sniper Said

After the torchlight red on rotting faces
The gnawing and the crying
Homestead and mall and reverberation
        of rifle-shots over the Appalachians
We who are living are now escaping

Here is no relief but only asphalt
The road pouring into a dead mountain mouth
Gravel of carious teeth
If there were mercy, but there are only zombies
        shambling behind the minivan

Red-tailed hawk staring from pine trees
But there is no mercy

I could be kinder to these creatures
        who do not comprehend human speech
        or that they are damaged and contagious.

My husband and children mourn but their pity
        scratches me like sleet rustling
        off the windshield, sticking to the grass.
They don't know the stakes. The sick
        want to pull you down.
Never get better. Hope could kill us all.
Someone has to face backwards, watching
        the city shrink, picking
        off the zombies who would follow.
Someone must ape the indifference of the dead.
My vigilance. For others, nostalgia,
        watching ice from a warm place
        as return becomes impossible.
A blizzard that passes understanding.

EARTH-TWO SONNET

A caped figure slips through an empty building, inked
    figment on the brink
of the place where General Lee, tired of fighting, swore
    to serve as president.
Books wait breathless in their boxes; renovation's
    imminent.
The blackboards ache like thunderclouds. Power trying
    to break.

At dinner, it's all doppelgangers and secret identities.
    Captain America's shield is the Marvel standard for durability,
he explains as our son lists mythic forces that might
    shatter its
flawlessness. Nova Heat from the Human Torch; Hulk's
    avocado fist.
Their mirror-faces glow. *Maybe Thor's hammer,* they agree.

May that hammer slam
this Earth-One heroine. Let her drop the shield, ride the
    bolt to a parallel dimension and learn
to be ordinary. Let the afternoon level its cosmic rays
    at my back, burn
the scar-shadow-stain of the last few years onto the
    linoleum,

sketching a record of the armor I recycle, the tights I now
  peel free.
Allowed to wrinkle; skip a meeting of the League; be
  indiscreet. Her perfection only legend now.
  Vibranium chip of history.

ACKNOWLEDGMENTS

I am grateful to the editors of the following journals, in which versions of these poems appear:

Fringe: Bicameral Woman, Book of Neurotransmitters, Rumpelstiltsken, Zombie Thanksgiving

Thanal: Just Long Enough to Hurt

Unsplendid: Earth-Two Sonnet

Verse Wisconsin: Villainous Creeds

This project was supported in part by the Lenfest Grant program at Washington and Lee University.

I heeded many voices as I wrote these poems, some of them belonging to my wonderful colleagues, especially Suzanne Keen, Ellen Mayock, Deborah Miranda, and Jeanine Silveira Stewart. Warm thanks to Nathalie Anderson, Asali Solomon, and Kath Wilham who helped me with "The Receptionist" at different stages; to Scott Nicolay, Anna Lena Phillips, and Margo Solod, whose advice improved many of the "other tales"; and to members of the Discussion of Women's Poetry List for cheering me on, particularly Lawrence Schimel, who urged me to submit the manuscript to fabulous Aqueduct Press. Other boon quest companions include Ann Fisher-Wirth, Cynthia Hogue, Janet McAdams, Tinni Sen, Rosemary Starace, and my mother and sister, Patricia Cain Wheeler and Claire Kerr. "Rumpelstiltsken" is for Ellen Satrom, Paul Hanstedt, and Lucy. Years of reading aloud with Madeleine and Cameron underpin "The Receptionist," so my debt to that canon is enormous, but I'm not sure I would have written the sequence without the inspiration of Diana Wynne Jones' *Tough Guide to Fantasyland*. Chris Gavaler and I have alternately played master and hero for one another for many years: owe him most of all, I do.

Biography

Lesley Wheeler is the author of *Heterotopia* (winner of the Barrow Street Press Poetry Prize), Heathen, Voicing American Poetry, and other books. With Moira Richards, Rosemary Starace, and others, she coedited the anthology *Letters to the World: Poems from the Wom-Po Listserv.* She maintains a blog on poetry's possible worlds at lesleywheeler.org and is the Henry S. Fox Professor of English at Washington and Lee University in Lexington, Virginia.

Proof

Made in the USA
Columbia, SC
20 April 2017